CHESS TALES

Improving & Coaching

Winning Tips for Young Players

Paul Dansey

P. Dansey

I hope this is of help
with your games

MAPLE
PUBLISHERS

Chess Tales: Winning Tips for Young Players

Author: Paul Dansey

Copyright © Paul Dansey (2022)

The right of Paul Dansey to be identified as author of this work has been asserted by the author in accordance with section 77 and 78 of the Copyright, Designs and Patents Act 1988.

First Published in 2022

ISBN 978-1-915492-65-4 (Paperback)
     978-1-915492-66-1 (E-Book)

Book Cover Design and Layout by:
    White Magic Studios
    www.whitemagicstudios.co.uk

Published by:
    Maple Publishers
    1 Brunel Way,
    Slough,
    SL1 1FQ, UK
    www.maplepublishers.com

PREFACE

Chess coaching has given me much enjoyment for the last forty years, especially in observing many young players reach adulthood and become better players than I could ever achieve. I have had a special interest in encouraging more girls to play and continue playing chess because it is traditionally a male dominated pursuit in the UK as was women's football until recently. The chess world is international and open to all though traditional barriers may still need to be overcome. I have found inspiration and encouragement from chess colleagues whose paths have crossed mine and I thank all of them and those I have played with at club/tournament level. By both playing and teaching chess I have improved my game. Playing chess both challenges and excites me. What will happen in my next game of chess is uncertain but whatever the result my game will improve especially if I am challenged. As with any competitive game or sport it is hard losing but after the initial disappointment the aim is to learn from any mistakes and become a better player. This applies to all age groups because we never stop learning whether you are a young chess player or a chess coach. My aim of writing these stories is to aid the learning of players by adding a little variety and fun for young players. We all learn differently and some of you will learn by participation and others will learn of beginnings, endings and middle games visually by watching games on YouTube and seeing how the pieces on the chess board move. Perhaps you may find it easier to read books or by playing over past games. Alternatively you may learn by a mix of these methods or being inspired by your chess coach. Whether you play for interest and to challenge yourself or in a team I hope you will continue to enjoy playing chess.

Information for the Reader

Some of the stories are based on chess legends which I have adapted.

The chapters need not be read in order but according to experience and interest. Some of the chapters have game scores in the algebraic notation and this is explained in chapter seven. The following chapters then use algebraic notation.

Contents

ABOUT THE AUTHOR

I thank my father for teaching me to play chess when I was 9 years old. I continued to play chess casually at school and college and later in my work place there was an informal chess group set up after increased interest with the World Chess Championship in 1972 between challenger Bobby Fischer of the USA and defending champion Boris Spassky of the Soviet Union. At work in lunch breaks we played five minute games and it toned my skills and improved my knowledge of chess openings. In 1978 I played anxiously in my first weekend chess tournament and subsequent to this I joined a local club where I soon became interested in helping younger players. I also started to help with after school chess clubs in the Cambridgeshire area where I was living at that time.

My chess rating improved when I played in more weekend tournaments. I became Junior Organiser for the East Anglian Chess Union in the 1980s and I organised junior training events having qualified as a British Chess Federation (now the English Chess Federation) junior coach. In the mid-eighties I was elected to represent the East Anglian Chess Union on the British Chess Federation's Management Board which gave me insight that politics applies to most endeavours. I have played in chess teams in first the Huntingdon and Peterborough Chess League, then for Norfolk and more recently in the Merseyside League. I thank all my local clubs for their encouragement. The pandemic encouraged me to play online chess which is now my main interest.

I have published articles on information science (my previous profession before retirement), conchology and family history. I have previously published a book based on the letters of Captain William Dansey (Trotman Publishing, 2010). ISBN9781907417054)

ACKNOWLEDGEMENTS

Diagrams and illustrations

I appreciated the assistance of two websites:

publicdomainpictures.net for the illustrations.

jinchess.com for setting up chess diagrams.

My Thanks

The inspiration for this book was all the young people in my local chess club and an independent school where I have more recently coached. I thank all my chess colleagues who assisted with these clubs for their encouragement.

I thank the White Magic Studios' team for all their invaluable help in bringing these stories to a wider audience.

I give special thanks to my wife, Rosie, a non-chess player, for her help with the editing and her helpful suggestions to improve the book's readability from her experience of working with young people.

A NOTE FOR CHESS COACHING

My aim of writing these stories is to aid the learning of players and when I coached chess I often began sessions by reading one of the stories to introduce or remind players of how the pieces move. At times the young people participated. For instance in chapter one, the story of chess, rice can be measured into mugs and bags to see the enormity of the task or chapter five where Alice becomes a Queen, can be a live chess game. Young people can represent the chess pieces and make their moves which are a fun way of learning. I found these ideas gave variety to my coaching and introduced a lighter element into a game where concentration is the key. At times I have used chess notation as part of the story and this can be an easier way to introduce and learn chess notation or a way to become more confident in recording games. Coaches are welcome to use any of the ideas in the book.

Further Ideas

In my chess coaching I sometimes introduced a creative element by setting a competition before holidays, such as poems or stories about chess. Artistic skills can be encouraged by making chess sets, using recycled materials, inspired by the true story and film, 'The Queen of Katwe'.

I apologise if I have made any errors in the game scores and recording notation.

INFORMATION ON CHESS PIECES

The Staunton chess set is the standard style of chess pieces recommended for use in competitions by FIDE, the international chess governing body.

If you visit the British Museum I suggest you view the Lewis chessmen there which were found on the Isle of Lewis in Scotland and were probably made in Norway. They consist of elaborately worked walrus ivory and whales' teeth in the form of seated Kings and Queens, mitred bishops, knights on horses and standing pawn obelisks as the following illustration shows. Their discovery was some time before 1831.

INTRODUCTION

One day I saw a chess board in the shop window of an antique shop. The chess pieces on it were all different shapes and sizes. They were made from plastic, metal and wood. The shop keeper did not have a complete set of 32 pieces but he had bought pieces as he came across them in sales over the years.

At night after the shop closed the chess pieces came alive and told each other these tales.

A King told the first story. He was shaped as an Indian Rajah sitting on a throne.

Chapter 1

The Story of Chess

The King's story was how the game of chess was invented in India about 1400 years ago, a very long time ago.

Once upon a time over a thousand years ago in India there lived a young King called Shirham who had only recently succeeded his father to the throne. He thought his main purpose in life was to be a warrior and to lead his armies in battle against other kingdoms.

The King's wars with neighbouring kingdoms meant that the armies from these kingdoms invaded his own kingdom, killing the young farmers and carrying off the women and children as slaves. The armies of elephants and horses trampled down the crops and there were not enough people left to grow many crops so the whole country was becoming poorer. At the same time the wars were expensive and the King had to raise taxes to pay for all his wars. The people could not afford to pay the increased taxes as their crops had been destroyed. The King's Advisors were in despair and the Chief Advisor said to the others "What can we do to persuade King Shirham to stop making war as this is making the kingdom poorer?"

Now in one of the villages of the kingdom there lived a young woman called Leela. Her parents had died during the recent wars and she and her oldest brother, Dakshi, were trying to care for their younger brothers and sisters. Dakshi decided to go to the King's court and see if he could join the King's Army. An old man in the village offered to marry Leela and said that he would take care of the family. Leela did not care for this old man and thought he is trying to get hold of the family land so she also went to the court to see if she could get a job there. Her brother, Dakshi, managed to find work for her as a servant caring for the King's children. She taught the royal children a board game that she had invented to show her young brothers and sisters about the war in which Dakshi was involved in as a soldier of the King.

One day the King Shirham visited his children and found them playing this new board game. At first he was angry because he thought they were playing a gambling game as many board games in those days involved gambling. The King's oldest son said, "Father it is not a gambling game but a game of mind skill." He showed his father how to play. "Father this game is a war game. This square board with 64 smaller squares on it is the field of battle and it is a game between two opponents. Each player has an army of 16 men. On the first row in front of each player are 8 important pieces. In the middle of the row are a King and his Chief Advisor. Then there are two war elephant mounted warriors and on either side next to them are two horse mounted warriors. At the two corner squares are war chariots. In front of the Officers and King in the next row are 8 foot soldiers. Each player moves in turn and the game finishes when the enemy King is captured and killed."

The oldest son showed his father how each piece moved and how to capture the King. They played some games and at first the son won all the games but then he let his father win some and later on when the King became better at the game he sometimes won a game fairly. King Shirham was so pleased with the game he asked how the son knew how to play this new game. His son told him about the young woman servant, Leela, who had brought the new game to court.

Now all the Advisors and other people at court had to learn the game and when King Shirham played against them they let him win so he wanted some harder competition and he invited a neighbouring King over to visit. Shirham showed him how to play the game and at first King Shirham won all the games but the neighbouring King went away to practice and the next time he came to visit he was able to win some of the games. Soon all the other Kings learnt about the game and they were soon all so busy playing the new game that they forgot about fighting battles with real armies and were content to play with pretend armies. The King's oldest son suggested a big tournament with all the Kings and Advisors playing in it and because Shirham had the help of Leela as coach he was able to win the international tournament.

King Shirham was now very pleased with himself. His country was recovering from all the wars and becoming rich again and the people were able to afford the taxes so the King could afford a lot of clothes and other pleasures for himself and family. He said to Leela "What a wonderful game you have given us, what reward can I give you? You can have anything you ask for." He was hoping that Leela would not ask for anything too expensive.

Leela thought for a moment and then put down a chess board in front of King Shirham and said, "I need some rice for myself and my village. I would like one grain of rice for the first square in the left hand corner of the first row, then two grains for the second square and four grains for the third square and so on doubling the number of grains each time until you reach the 64th square." Well the King thought this would only involve a few thousand grains of rice and there must be at least that in a sack of rice so he agreed to give Leela that reward. He told his Chief Advisor to go off and get the servants to count the grains of rice out. The Chief Advisor was not so sure about it being such a small amount of rice but he thought a few sacks might be sufficient.

When the servants started the task they found that after a while it was taking them a long time to count the grains. The first square had one grain, the next two grains, the third square

4 grains, the fourth 8 grains, the fifth 16 grains, the sixth 32 grains, the seventh 64 grains, the eighth 128 grains, the ninth 256 grains, so the tenth square needed 512 grains which took a long time to count out. One of the servants, who was a good calculator, said, "One cup holds about one thousand grains and one bag takes four cups so let us measure it out by cup and bag." So they then found that the eleventh square took one cup, the twelfth square two cups and the thirteenth one small bag of rice. The fourteenth square required two bags of rice and so on.

They soon found that they had used up a sack of rice and had to fetch some more sacks from the Royal store room. The storekeeper became worried and went to tell the Chief Advisor. The Chief Advisor now came down to where the servants were counting out the rice to see why they needed so much. The clever servant told the Chief Advisor that they would soon use up all the sacks from the King's store room and would have to get some more sacks from the National Granary which held as much rice as one hundred store rooms.

The Chief Advisor was now very worried and asked the clever servant, who was good at arithmetic, how much rice would they need to meet the reward that Leela had asked for. When he was told he was astonished and said, "You can carry on but I need to talk to the King about it." The Chief Advisor went to the King and said, "Sir, I am afraid that I have miscalculated how much rice we will need to provide to Leela to reward her." He then explained how with each square doubling the amount of rice, that all the rice in the National Granary would be insufficient to meet Leela's reward. "How many National Granaries would we need?" asked King Shirham and went on to say that maybe the answer was to conquer and take over some nearby kingdoms and take their rice. The advisor replied that even if they were able to conquer all the kingdoms in the world they would still not have enough rice.

Shirham now became very angry because he saw how foolish he had been in promising a reward he could not fulfil. Angrily he said, "The woman has tricked me. If I have her killed I will not have to give the reward." The Chief Advisor agreed that this was one solution to the problem but then they might stop other people showing the King new inventions. He suggested to King Shirham that he could go and talk to Leela and see if he could persuade her to change the reward.

The Chief Advisor went to Leela and said, "We need you to come and check the amount of rice so that we do not give you too much or too little. Will you come and count out the rice with us?" "Oh!" said Leela, "You have found me out. You know that we would not have sufficient time in a lifetime to count all the rice grain by grain. I only wanted to teach the King not to make hasty decisions and listen to advice before he acts." The Chief Advisor agreed that this was a good lesson but what did Leela want as a reward instead. Leela now said, "If the King agrees to bring a sack of rice and meet me alone on the outskirts of my village and stay with me for a day and act as my servant that will be sufficient reward."

King Shirham agreed to this and met Leela near her village. His servants left a sack of rice and left them together. Leela said to the King. "Go into that hut where you will find some servant clothes to change into so that you can fulfil the tasks I give you and no one will know who you are so that you will not feel embarrassed acting as my servant for a day." King Shirham changed into an old tunic and trousers and old sturdy shoes. Leela said, "Now we need to go to my village and please carry the sack of rice." Although the King was quite fit and healthy because he was used to fighting in battles, he was not used to carrying sacks of rice and he was quite tired after walking for a mile to the village.

When they got to the village the villagers all gathered around Leela and the King whom they thought was Lela's servant. Lela said that the King had sent them some rice and the servant would share it out. One young woman came forward who was a widow because her husband had been killed in the recent wars. Next came a man who had lost a leg in the war and another man was blind because of the fighting. The rice was therefore shared out with all the people who were unable to work the fields and grow their own crop of rice. When the people had gone away back to their huts Leela said to King Shirham, "We must now get some rice for our meal which you will gather for me from the field over there." This was hard work for the King especially as he cut his hands picking the rice and his trousers and shoes were getting very muddy. Then Leela added some herbs and lentils and made their meal. It was not much to eat but King Shirham was hungry after carrying the sack of rice and harvesting the rice so he gulped down the meal.

After the meal Leela asked the King if he would like to play a game of chess and he agreed. He thought perhaps he would have his revenge by beating her at chess. In the middle of the game King Shirham thought that Leela had made a mistake and that he could make an easy capture of a piece but this time he did not rush to make the move. He said to himself that Leela does not often make mistakes and perhaps it is a trick. So he looked at the position a bit longer and realised that if he rushed out and captured Leela's piece he would leave a hole in his own defences and that Leela's pieces would then rush in through the hole and capture his King and win the game. He found a better move and eventually won the game. This is good advice to all chess players to stop and think before making a move.

The Royal servants met them at the edge of the village at the end of the day and King Shirham returned to his palace a much wiser man. From then on there were no more wars. The country became very rich and the King had learnt to always listen to good advice and think of his peoples' welfare as well as his own. He generally found that decisions that were good for his people were also good for him and so they lived happily ever after.

Chapter 2

The Battling Bishops

The next night one of the Bishops, a black wooden piece, told his story.

Once upon a time, there were two bishops who were brothers. Ever since they were children they had fought each other. Even when they were grownup and church leaders they still did not get on well together.

One day they both discovered a square island. Both bishops liked to eat a ploughman's lunch consisting of a glass of beer and a cheese and pickle sandwich. The island that they came upon grew the fruit and wheat needed for making a ploughman's lunch. The land of the square island was divided into four smaller square areas. One area was good for producing beer; a second area was good for bread, a third for cheese and the last area for pickles.

The bishops began to fight each other for control of the island. First one bishop got control of more than half the island but the other bishop fought back and also won control of more than half the island. They fought and fought until they had fought to a standstill. Whilst they were pausing in their fight the King came up and said, "Stop fighting. I have worked out a way for you to divide the island between you so that you each will have land for producing all four parts of your ploughman's lunches."

"The island is going to be divided into 64 small squares. You will each move diagonally across the squares. One bishop will move only on one set of 32 squares which will belong to him and the other bishop will own the remaining 32 squares. You will never move onto a square owned by your brother but you will have access to 8 squares that produce beer, 8 that produce cheese, 8 that produce bread and 8 that produce pickles. You will never meet so you cannot then fight each other anymore."

So this both explains how the chequer board was invented on which we play chess and draughts but also explains why the bishop's move diagonally in a chess game. It may help you remember which way to move your two bishops.

Chapter 3

Those Naughty Knights

For a change one chilly evening a shiny Knight read out a poem.

Oh! Those naughty Knights,

They jump here and there,

They catch us unaware.

Oh! Those naughty Knights,

The Queen fears their attack,

She cannot check them back.

Oh! Those naughty Knights,
The King cannot block a Knight's check.

Oh! Those naughty Knights,
The Bishops and Rooks find them annoying.

Oh! Those naughty Knights,
The Pawns try to drive the Knights away
But they jump back another way.

Oh! Those naughty Knights,
Treason! Treason! A Knight has forked
their Majesties. Off with his head!

Oh! Those naughty Knights,
They think it neat
To make a smothered mate.
Oh! Those naughty knights.

Paul Dansey (2015)

Chapter 4

Alice becomes a Queen

One of the magnificent Queen pieces told this story on a cold and windy evening, the kind of evening when we all like to snuggle up and listen to a story. She told of a chess game where Alice is a white pawn but is hoping to become a Queen.

1.

"Phew!" said Alice," that was close. Thank you for saving me from that nasty black Queen. I assume that I will not become a Queen because the black King is occupying the square that I want to get to. Will it be a draw?"

"No," said the white King." The last move by the black King was a mistake. I can see a way to win. Follow me!"

Reader: Can you see what move white makes next?

The answer is in the next diagram.

2.

"I do not want to move," said the black King. "I am happy to stay where I am."

"No!" said the white King. "You have to move. It is your turn to move. According to the rules of chess we must move in turn. You are not allowed to miss a turn."

"Oh! Alright I shall move," said the black King," but I shall keep near this square so Alice cannot reach it."

3.

Reader: Can you see what white plays next?

See the next diagram for the answer.

4.

The black King has to move again but he stays near the promotion square.

5.

The white King now says to Alice." You can move forward now but do not worry about the black King. Take hold of my hand and I will protect you."

So Alice moved forward one square and poked at the black King with her short sword. "Check," she said. "Ouch!" said the black King. "I shall gobble you up."

The white King said, "You cannot take Alice because I am holding her hand and if you take her you will be on the square next to me and that is not allowed. Opposite coloured Kings cannot touch."

6.

So the black King had to retreat but he was still near the promotion square.

7.

The white King now said to Alice, "You can move forward to the next square and check the black King again."

8.

The black King said "Ouch!" again and moved up besides Alice so he was no longer at the end of her sword. He was hungrily eying Alice.

9.

The white King now said to Alice, "You can move on to the promotion square. What piece would you like to be promoted to? You can choose between a knight, a bishop, a rook, or a Queen?"

"A Queen of course," said Alice.

Alice now found herself getting taller and larger and her sword was growing longer so that she could reach in all directions. She also felt a crown growing on her head.

She now could reach behind her and said check to the black King.

10.

Reader: Can the black King take her?

The black King was not allowed to capture Alice because she was still protected by her King so he moved back out of check.

11.

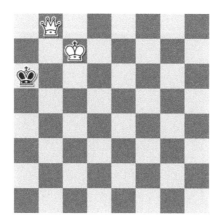

Now reader, can you see the next move which was checkmate?

12.

"Hurray!" said Alice. "I became a queen and with the next move I checkmated the black King."

Reader: Do you think you will remember this game and how the checkmate came about?

Chapter 5

A Christmas Chess Story

A pawn told this story when it was Christmas Eve and the chess pieces were feeling a little sad that no one had bought them as a Christmas present so they could be played with in a new home. First he tried to cheer them all up by cheekily asking, "Who lives at the North Pole? Answer: Santa Claus."

It was early Christmas Eve in Santa's workshop. The enormous room was filled with toys and other presents ready for delivery by Santa. In one area there were piles of chess sets. As it was a magical time the toys were able to come alive. A little plastic pawn climbed out of his plastic box. He looked around there were thousands of plastic chess sets piled up to the ceiling. Nearby he saw another chess set where the pieces were made of gold and silver and covered in precious stones: diamonds, sapphires, rubies and emeralds. Standing by this jewelled box was the figure of a warrior carrying a spear and shield. He was made of gold and also covered in sparkling stones. He said, "I am a very important king's pawn and my set is going to be a present for an Arab prince. We are worth over a million pounds." The plastic pawn was amazed.

Nearby he saw a wooden set with a wooden pawn with a similar shape to the plastic pawn but made of polished rosewood. This wooden pawn said, "My set is going to be used in the next World Chess Championship and it costs over a thousand pounds." The plastic pawn was very impressed but he went back to his box, feeling sad and very unimportant.

Santa came round and said to the little pawn, "Do not be sad. You are going to be in the stocking of a young chess player who has asked me especially for a chess set so they can practice at home and improve for when they play games at their junior chess club. I have had letters from lots of young chess players asking for chess books or chess sets for Christmas so they can get better at playing this wonderful game. The jewelled chess set and the championship chess set are not going to be used much but your set is going to have a lot of use. You are going to give a lot of fun to the young chess player. So remember all pawns are important."

Chapter 6

Teamwork and Useful Pieces

This evening the chess pieces were having a discussion on who was the most useful chess piece as they sat in their position on the chess board and the remaining odd pieces were surrounding them. All were sitting up trying to look important.

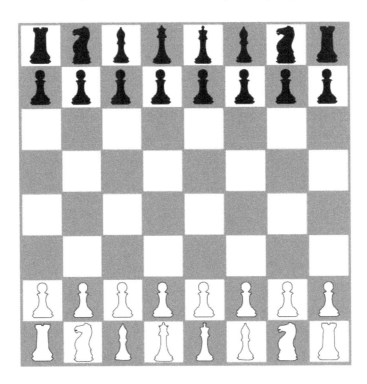

The knight spoke first, "I am a useful piece because with my trusty steed I can jump over other pieces and I am the only piece that can do a smothered mate."

Then the bishop said, "I am a useful piece because I move along the diagonals and can go from one corner to the opposite corner in one move."

The pawn piped up, "Although I am little there are eight of us and when we form a pawn chain we are very strong. Also if I get to the eighth square I can be promoted to a knight or a bishop or a rook or even a Queen."

The rook growled, "I can move up and down or side to side. Like the bishop I can move from side to side in one move. I can move onto all the 64 squares but the bishop is restricted to one colour square so he can only go onto 32 squares."

The Queen now put a word in, "I am a very powerful piece but I often need the help of other pieces to checkmate the enemy King."

The King then spoke with authority, "Although I can only move by one square in any direction except when castling I am a useful piece in the ending. We are all useful pieces but we are even more useful when we work together as a team. So remember chess playing involves teamwork."

So the pieces now all said together, "Chess means teamwork!"

This is very useful advice to remember in your games especially when you are playing in a team.

Chapter 7

Chess Basics

Board Set Up

The chess board should be a chequer board with alternating light and dark squares as shown below. It is set up so that each player has a dark square at the corner nearest their left hand and a light square on the corner nearest their right hand. See the next diagram.

Black Player

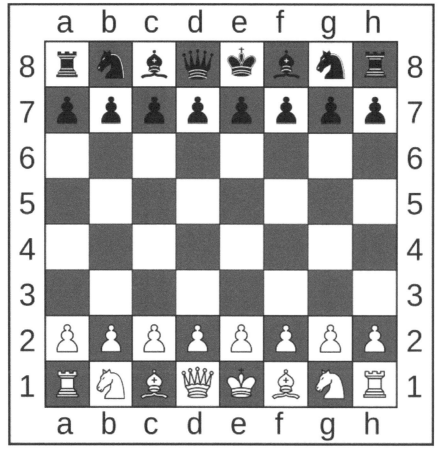

White Player

Each of the 64 small squares of the chess board is named using coordinates like a map reference. It is made from the white player's point of view. See the above diagram. The squares are named using the letters below white's side of the board.

After the letter (a-h) is the number of the rank that the square is on. The numbers are from 1 to 8 and shown on the left side of the board from the white player's point of view. So the square on the left hand corner of the board nearest white's left hand is named a1. This square is at the start of rank 1. The square at the nearest corner to white's right hand is named h1. The letters are also the names of files of squares leading ahead from white's side of the board so square a1 is also the start of a file of squares going up to square a8 on the corner nearest black's right hand.

There are four squares at the centre of the board. The two squares at the centre on white's half of the board are named d4 and e4. The other two centre squares on black's half of the board are named d5 and e5.

When the players are sitting at the board at the start of the game the major pieces occupy rank number one for white and rank number eight for black. The 8 white pawns are arrayed along the second rank in front of the major pieces. The 8 black pawns are arrayed along the seventh rank. The ranks nearest to each player are called back ranks. A player may say that they obtained a back rank mate with a Queen or rook.

Setting up the pieces to start a game

The diagram below shows how the pieces are arranged on the board at the start of a game. White always has the first move in competitive chess. Note the colour of the corner squares on the right hand of each player. It is a light square. Also a white Queen is always starting on square d1 which is a light colour.

Scoring a game using algebraic notation

A move in the game scored using algebraic notation gives the name of the piece, the square it is moving from and the square it is moving to. The moves are also numbered so at the start of a game the white player moves first and the move is number 1. Also white's move is placed immediately following the number 1 and black's move in reply is also their first move so there is two or three character spaces after the record of white's move. Each major piece is identified by a capital letter.

The letter K for a King, letter Q for a Queen, letter R for a rook, letter B for a bishop, letter N for a knight as the letter K has been used for the King. The pawns are not identified by P but just the named squares they are moving between are used. A capture is shown by capital X. An en passant capture has e.p following the score.

Castling King side is identified by 0-0 and Queenside castling by 0-0-0. Note for castling I am using the zero character,0, rather than a capital O. A check is noted by following the characters by + and a checkmate by ++. Sometimes a good move is followed by ! and a bad move by ? or even ??. An interesting or unusual move by !?

When a pawn is promoted by getting to end of the board it is notated by e8=Q to denote that a white pawn has got to square e8 and has been promoted to a Queen.

If there is some ambiguity of which piece is being moved then their starting square is indicated. For example if there are two knights one on b1 and the other on f3 and they could both go to d2 then the move is notated by either Nbd2 or Nfd2 depending which knight moves. If one of the knight moves was forbidden because of exposing their King to a check it is clear which knight is moved without having to indicate their starting square.

This is an example of the opening 10 moves on both sides of a game.

1. e4 e5 2. Nf3 Nf6

(White has played the pawn in front of his King two squares forward to the centre of the board. Black has also moved his King's pawn to the centre of the board. White has the moved the knight on g1 to the square f3 and black has defended his pawn on e5 by moving his knight from b8 to c6).

3. Bc4 Nf6 4. d3 Bc5 5. c3 d6 6. 0-0 0-0 7. a4 a6 8. h3 h6 9. Bb3 Ba7 10. Nbd2 Nh5

Basic Concepts

For the benefit of improving chess players I use the acronym mnemonic, **KCD** as the first basic concept with K standing for the safety of the King, C for control of the centre and D for developing your pieces to attack and defend.

In the openings players realise there are thousands of variations so that it is difficult to remember them all. So there are various things to bear in mind as do's and don'ts.

Opening first with a Queen's pawn or King's pawn is highly recommended because it makes space for bishop and Queen moves. Knights should be developed towards the centre as there they fight for control of more space. In general knights are moved out before bishops. Do not make too many pawn moves as it wastes moves. It is advisable not develop the queen too early. Get the King safely castled as soon as possible. Fighting for control of the centre squares e4, d4, e5 and d5 is essential. Gambits often enable more rapid development of the bishops and knights.

MST is an acronym mnemonic for the second concept which is M for material gain; S for space gain and T for tempo gain. Tempo is a gain of a move if your opponent wastes a move by having to move a piece twice, especially in the opening.

A beginner chess player first learns the value of the pieces. So a pawn is worth one point, bishops and knights are worth three points, rooks worth five points and the Queen worth 9 points. So you can gain material by either capturing an enemy for nothing or exchanging a lower value piece for a higher value piece. This is called gaining the exchange. So capturing a knight but losing a pawn is a gain of two points and capturing a Queen but losing a rook is a four point gain.

Experienced players also try to gain space by placing their pieces on a square where they control more squares.

An example of a gain in tempo is in gambit opening variations. An example is the Scotch Gambit opening which goes as follows: 1. e4 e5 2. Nf3 Nc6 3. d4 eXd 4. Bc4. White has brought out his bishop rather than recapturing a pawn by NXd4. White having brought out a knight and bishop is now able to castle quickly. Black is at least two moves away from castling as his knight on g8 and the bishop on f8 have not been developed yet. The word gambit is derived from wrestling where an opponent is tripped up by a leg. This tripping is expressed in Italian as *dare il gambetto*.

To gain an advantage in high level chess you cannot expect your opponent will carelessly lose material so you instead manoeuvre to gain space and tempi. Often material, space and tempi can be traded. So a player may sacrifice a pawn to gain a tempo or to clear space for the long range action of their bishop or rook or Queen. An experienced player can often by looking at the position in a game decide which player has an advantage in the control of space even if the material balance is equal.

SWOT is an acronym mnemonic for the third basic concept where S stands for Strengths; W for weaknesses; O for opportunities and T to identify any threats. The SWOT strategy is a business tool for making decisions that you can to use in chess to decide on your moves.

The three basic concepts are applied in master games. A selection of these games is shown in chapter nineteen.

Opening

Chess players should always have a plan of campaign. They try to gain an advantage in the opening by knowing the variations better than their opponent or making a new move that they have found out for themselves or by looking at recent master games. It is best to decide what first move to make if you have the white pieces and plan how to deal with the different defences that your opponent with the black pieces may use.

When you are black you need to decide what defence you will make to e4 or d4 as they are the most common opening moves by white. You gradually learn defences to other first moves by white such as c4, Nf3, g3. With other first moves by white just try to develop your pieces, keep your King safe and try to contest the centre.

Middle Game

After the opening has been carried out you need to know how to handle the middle game. This involves making a plan. You often have to adjust your plan as you go along but the same principles apply like keeping your King safe, contesting the centre and trying to get your pieces of squares where they control space.

Chess is a mind sport but also a craft where you learn from the masters. The game involves taking decisions on each move. Using SWOT look at the position on the board access where you and your opponent are strong, (S) and where there are weaknesses (W). Look for opportunities (O) to attack but also look for threats (T) by your opponent. Look at the pawn structures. Are there strong pawn chains; doubled or isolated pawns; isolated pawns; backward pawns etc.? Consider where the Kings are. Are they well protected or vulnerable to attack?

These all should all be considered in making your plan.

End Game

Simple end games are when all the major pieces have left the board and just the Kings are left and one or a few pawns. The aim here is for one of the pawns to be promoted to Queen or rook so that the player has sufficient material to make a checkmate. To advance a pawn to be promoted the player has to gain space at the expense of the defending King. Often this involves gaining what is called the opposition. An example is shown in the chapter four. An example of an ending with Queen and King versus a lone King is in chapter fourteen. Rook and King versus the opposing King is shown in chapter fifteen. Check mates can be made with two bishops and King versus a lone King. This has to be learnt so practice versus another player or a computer. Remember this has to be done within 50 moves on each side if not it is a draw. Also you have to avoid a three time repetition of a position with the same player having a move. You can find the rules of competitive chess in other books or on the internet. In an ending with knight, bishop and King versus a King it is possible with difficulty to get a checkmate within the 50 move rule but it is often a draw if the players are short of time on the chess clock. Rook and one pawn versus rook are wins or draws depending on the positions of the Kings. Examples are shown in chapter 17 on Exercises.

After each game if you have kept score it is good advice to take time to analyse your game and see if you could have made better moves. This is a good way of learning.

⸺⊰◇⊱⸺

Chapter 8

Restless Rooks

One of the rooks decided to tell his tale next.

The rook pieces are shaped like a castle so some people call them castle pieces not a rook.

Aunt Mary was visiting the home of her 10 year old nephew, John, in order to play their monthly game of chess. She waited sitting at the chess board in the dining room. When John arrived she said to him,

"John! I have just been listening to complaints about you by your rook pieces. They say that you just move your knights, bishops and Queen and do not let them join in the game. You either get checkmate without their help or blunder away your Queen and resign."

John said, "I find it difficult to use the rooks much because they are stuck in the corner and blocked from moving by my pawns and the other back rank pieces."

Aunt Mary now explained how to involve the rooks in the game. The central pawns in front of the King and Queen are usually moved first and often exchanged so that you have open files in the middle of the board. The rooks should be centralised as soon as possible after moving your central pawns and developing your other pieces.

"I will show you a game played by a famous American chess master, Paul Morphy, against a team of two amateur players. It was played in a box in an opera house in Paris in 1858."

The Game of Paul Morphy versus Duke Karl and Count Isouard

1.	e4	e5
2.	Nf3	d6 (Phildor's defence)
3.	d4	Bg4
4.	dXe	BXf3
5.	QXf3	dXe
6.	Bc4	Nf6 (mate on f7 is threatened)
7.	Qb3	Qe7 (guards f7)
8.	Nc3	c6 (White did not grab the pawn on b7 because of Qb4+ leading to an ending with only one pawn up.)
9.	Bg5	b5? (They need to get their king safe.)
10.	NXb5	cXb
11.	BXb5+	Nbd7 (White gives up a knight for two pawns but has a strong attack.)
12.	0-0-0	Rd8
13.	RXd7	RXd7
14.	Rd1	Qe6
15.	BXd7+	NXd7
16.	Qb8+	NXb8
17.	Rd8++	

Chapter 9

Pawns are Important

"Pawns are the soul of chess. They alone form the attack and defence; on their good or bad situation depends on the gain or loss of each party."

(Francois Philidor 1726-1795)

A small plastic pawn was feeling lonely and unimportant. Another pawn who was even smaller in height reminded her of the following qualities of pawns to try and cheer her up and help make her a stronger piece.

1. A pawn is worth one point and these points can add up.

2. A pawn can move forward one or two squares in its first move.

3. They can only move forwards but not backwards.

4. They capture diagonally one square forward.

5. The *en passant* rule which prevents the pawn being bypassed by an opposing pawn.

6. When they reach the end of the board they can be promoted to a knight, bishop, rook or Queen.

7. A pawn always controls at least one or two squares diagonally ahead of itself.

8. When a pawn moves forward it loses control of one or two squares but then gains control of one or two squares in its new position.

9. Isolated pawns are weak.

10. Double pawns are weak.

11. Pawns are stronger when they are joined together in a chain. The weakest point of a pawn chain is the base pawn.

12. When pawns have the chance of a recapture it is best to capture towards the centre of the board.

13. Two pawns next to each other which are only 2 squares away from promotion are worth at least a rook if it is their move.

14. A pawn blocks one rank and one file (explained in chapter seven, Chess Basics).

15. When a pawn moves forward it no longer blocks one rank but blocks another rank (see chapter seven).

16. When a pawn captures it changes the file it is on and opens its old file but blocks a new one.

17. A protected passed pawn is strong.

By now the pawn was smiling and feeling very important. The above features helped her realise how she could contribute to the team so she would be less lonely. She now aimed to become a stronger piece.

Chapter 10

The Knight's Tale

All the chess pieces were interested to learn more about the game of chess they played in and these stories were beginning to make them feel important. They were no longer dusty chess pieces sitting in an antique shop waiting for a buyer. They looked forward to the evening when another story would be told.

The shiny gold Knight was the next to tell his story.

He told of a smothered check mate played about 400 years ago by an Italian Chess Master, called Gioachino Greco. He recorded some of his games against weaker players but did not name them so I have named these as unknown.

A smothered check mate is when the King is surrounded by his own pieces and cannot move out of being checked by a Knight as explained below by using chess notation.

Unknown	**Gioachino Greco**
1. e4	e5
2. Nf3	Nc6
3. Bc4	Bc5
4. 0-0	Nf6
5. Re1	0-0
6. c3	Qe7
7. d4	eXd
8. e5	Ng4
9. cXd4	NXd4
10. NXd4	Qh4
11. Nf3	QXf2+
12. Kh1	Qg1+
13. NXg1	Nf2++

Chapter 11

The King's Checkmate

One evening the pieces were all boasting of the checkmates that they had made in past games. The King interrupted with his experience of playing many games.

The King said "Do you know that a King's move can be a checkmate as it was in this game that I will show you?"

Edward Lasker	Sir George Thomas
1. d4	e6
2. Nf3	f5
3. Nc3	Nf6
4. Bg5	Be7
5. BXf6	BXf6
6. e4	fXe
7. NXe4	b6

8.	Ne5	0-0
9.	Bd3	Bb7
10.	Qh5	Qe7
11.	QXh7+	KXh7
12.	NXf6+	Kh6
13.	Neg4+	Kg5
14.	h4+	Kf4
15.	g3+	Kf3
16.	Be2+	Kg2
17.	Rh2+	Kg1
18.	Kd2++	(or could have played 0-0-0++

Checkmate Position

Chapter 12

Scholar's Mate

A stately black bishop told this story one evening when it was just starting to become dark. His story was about a young girl called Jane who had once played these games with him when he was part of a chess set owned by a school.

Jane aged 10 had joined the after school chess club when she was 9 years old. She was quite a good chess player and often won games against other members of the club. The chess coach who organised the club told Jane and her parents about a junior chess competition for players under 11 that was going to be held at a nearby school at the end of term. The coach suggested that Jane be entered in the competition. The completion would be held from 10.00 a.m. to 4.00 p.m. and there would be six games to be played by each player. Each game would last about 40 minutes with breaks between each round and a long break at lunch time. The entry fee was £5 and the top prize was £100. So Jane's parents agreed for her to be entered into the competition.

In the first game Jane had the black pieces and it went like this.

First opponent	Jane
1. e4	e5

(Jane knew that it was a good idea to push a centre pawn forward so that her bishop and Queen could get into the game,)

2. Bc4	Bc5 (Jane was more used to white playing Nf3 but she decided to copy her opponent's move.)
3. Qh5	(This was a surprise to Jane. Her coach had told her to bring out her knights and bishops before moving her Queen so she decided to move her knight and attack the enemy Queen but she missed what her opponent was threatening.)
	Nf6
4. QXf7++	Checkmate

So that game was finished early and Jane was very upset. She could not go home because her parents were meeting her at the tournament venue at lunch time.

She thought she would try this trick herself in the next game.

Jane had white in the next game so it went as follows.

Jane	Second opponent
1. e4	e5
2. Qh5	g6
3. Qxe5+	Qe7
4. QXh8	(Jane eventually won that game)

As Jane had won she was feeling better by the lunch break when her parents joined her for their picnic lunch. Many supportive parents have to give up their leisure time at weekends to transport young players to matches and some support them by staying through the day in the background.

After lunch Jane had the black pieces again. Jane had discussed her first two games with her coach. She was told the mate in her first game was called scholar's mate and her coach showed her ways to avoid it. We all learn from our mistakes and successes in games. The next game went as follows.

Third opponent	Jane
1. e4	e5
2. Qh5	Nc6
3. Bc4	Qe7

(Jane's Queen guards the pawn on f7 and stops a check mate.)

This was a longer game and ended in a draw.

The next game Jane had white.

Jane	Fourth opponent
1. e4	e5
2. Nf3	Nc6
3. Bc4	Bc5
4. 0-0	Nf6
5. d3	d6
6. Nc3	0-0
7. Bg5	Re8
8. Nd5	Be6
9. NXf6+	gXf
10. Be3	

Jane eventually won.

She lost her fifth game and drew her last game so she ended up on three points out of 6. This was a good result for her first competition and her chess coach and her parents all praised her for carrying on when she had at first lost a game and felt like going home.

Chapter 13

Double Checkmate

A plastic pawn in the Staunton pattern told this tale.

John was helping his mother with turning out the attic and came across a small wooden box. He looked inside and saw some pieces of carved wood which were different shapes and sizes. Some were dark brown and some light brown in colour. Others were shaped like a horse's head on a base. Two large pieces had a cross on top.

His mother, Mary, came over to see what he was looking at. "What are these?" asked John. "Oh" replied his mother, "I had forgotten that was up here. They are chess pieces."

"What is chess?" asked John.

His mother replied, "It is a board game of skill rather than chance. It is a game for two players played on a chequer board of 64 small squares. One person uses half the pieces which are light in colour and the other person uses the other half of pieces which are in a darker colour."

"Please, will you show me how to play chess," said John.

His mother replied, "Yes when we have finished working in the attic."

Later that day John and his mother sat down at a table and his mother found a wooden chequer board and took the chess pieces out of the box and showed John how the board was set up for the start of a game. She then told John the names of the pieces and how they moved with the object of the game being to checkmate the enemy King.

"When did you learn to play chess?" asked John.

His mother replied that she had learnt chess from her parents when she was aged 8. She also said that she had played as a King's pawn in a living chess display in the main town square of the capital city in front of the country's King and members of the Government and other important people.

She then told her son how this came about.

The Great Game

There was great excitement in the country. An International Chess Grandmasters' Tournament was to be played in the capital city and the World Chess Champion was one of the invited Grandmasters. The local champion was also invited.

It was decided that as part of the opening ceremony that a living chess match would be played between the World Champion and the local champion.

Mary's parents were part of a theatre group and they had been asked to provide actors to play the part of chess pieces in the living chess display. It was decided that Mary, aged 8, would have the part of the white King's pawn in front of her father who played the white King. The players chose lots for colours and the local champion had the white pieces.

Mary was the white King's pawn. She stood in front of her father who was playing the white King.

The local champion called out his first move.

It was pawn on the e2 squares moves forward two squares to the e4 square. So Mary moved forward two squares.

The World Champion called out my King's pawn forward two squares. The boy in front of the black King moved forward two squares to square e5 and now stood in front of and facing Mary. He towered over her but she knew he could do her no harm in this game.

The local champion now moved Mary's older sister, Jane, who was standing in front of their mother, the white Queen, two squares forward. The World Champion then captured Jane using the boy pawn in front of Mary. The local champion's next move was to move the boy standing on square c2 one square forward so as to threaten the black pawn on d4. The World Champion now used the pawn on d4 to capture the white pawn on c3. The local champion did not recapture but played his King's Bishop out to square c4. The World Champion instead of risking capturing another pawn developed his King's knight to the f6 square. The local champion offered another pawn by playing his King's knight to f3 so that he was ready to castle his King into safety.

The World Champion again did not risk capturing another pawn but played his King's bishop to c5. The local champion at last captured the pawn on c3 with his Queen's knight. He also now guarded Mary who was still on e4 from capture by the black knight on f6. The World Champion now played his Queen's pawn forward one square to square d6 to open lines for his Queen's bishop and also guarding his King's bishop. The local champion now castled his King to safety. The World Champion also castled.

The local champion now called out my knight on f3 goes to square g5. The World Champion pondered for a while and then played his King rook's pawn on h7 to square h6. The local champion now captured the pawn on f7 with his knight. The World Champion captured the knight with his rook. The local champion now told Mary on square e4 to move forward to square e5. Mary was now afraid that she would be captured by the pawn on d6 but the World champion instead moved his threatened knight on f6 to square g4. Mary was now told to move forward to square e6. "Oh, thought Mary. If I am not captured perhaps I will get to the eighth rank and be promoted to a Queen." The World Champion now played his Queen out to square h4 threatening Queen takes h2 mate. The local champion told Mary to capture the rook on f7 and check the black King. The World Champion now played his King to square f8 in front of Mary. The local champion then played his Queen's bishop to square f4, guarding the pawn on h2. The World Champion now captured the pawn on f2 with his knight. The local champion now played Mary's mother, the white Queen, to square e2. The World Champion now played his knight back to square g4, discovering a check by the black bishop on c5. The local champion now moved Mary's father, the white King out of check to square h1. The audience thought that the World Champion could go for perpetual check by knight back to f2 but the World Champion saw that this would risk being mated because the local champion could capture the knight with his rook on square f1 and if the World Champion captured on f2 with his Queen or bishop the local champion could play his Queen down to e8 mating the black King. The World Champion instead played his Queen's bishop to square d7. The local champion now played his Queen's rook on square a1 to square e1. The World Champion developed his Queen's knight to c6.

The local champion then told Mary's mother to swoop down to square e8 checking the black King. The World Champion now captured Mary's mother with his rook. The local champion now told Mary to capture the rook on e8 to revenge her mother and be promoted to a new Queen. Mary did not last long as a Queen because she was now captured by the World Champion's bishop. However, the local champion now played his Queen's bishop on f4 to capture the black pawn on d6 and announced double checkmate.

The Mayor of the capital city congratulated the local champion on his victory. The living chess players were all presented to the Mayor and he had a special word with Mary. He congratulated her on being promoted Queen and she said she did not mind being taken as the next move was checkmate in favour of the local champion.

<u>The Moves of the above Game</u>

Local Champion	World Champion
1. e4	e5
2. d4	exd
3. c3	dxc
4. Bc4	Nf6
5. Nf3	Bc5
6. Nxc3	d6
7. 0-0	0-0
8. Ng5	h6?
9. Nxf7	Rxf7
10. e5!	Ng4
11. e6	Qh4
12. exf+	Kf8
13. Bf4	Nxf2
14. Qe2	Ng4+
15. Kh1	Bd7
16. Rae1	Nc6
17. Qe8+!	Rxe8
18. fxe=Q+	Bxe8
19. Bxd6 mate	

Variations that could have been played

Variation A:

12. exf+   Kh7

13. Qd3+   g6

14. f8=N+   Kh8

15. Nxg6+ wins queen

Variation B

14. f8=N+   Kg7

15. Qxg6+   Kxf8

16. Qf7mate

Variation C

15. Kh1   Nf2+

16. RxN   BxR

17. Qe8 mate

A Note

This story is based on a game score from the one between Rezso Charousek versus Jakob Wollner (1893).

Chapter 14

A Queen's Mistake: Stalemate

A black Queen told this story of how she learnt to checkmate after being promoted from a pawn.

When this pawn was playing a game she had just been promoted to Queen so she was very inexperienced and did not know how to achieve a checkmate.

On the board there was just a white King versus a black King and Queen. The black King said that his Queen could not get a checkmate all by herself. She would need his help to cover escape squares. He said that the enemy King needed to be forced to a side of the board so that the King only had six squares available to move including the square he was standing on.

Somehow they got to this position with black to move.

"Good" said the black Queen," we have forced him into a corner I shall move and keep him there." "No," said the black,"let me move nearer." But the Queen was not listening so she moved to b3. "We have got you now," she said to the white King.

"No, you have not," said the white King. "I am not in check so it is not checkmate but I cannot move without being in check so it is a draw by stalemate."

The black Queen could have moved to b4 and then let her King make a move to c3 and then the black Queen would have mated the white King by moving to b2.

The white King needed to be allowed to move to and through between the a1 and a2 squares until he was mated.

Chapter 15

Ronnie Rook's Mate

One of the rooks called Ronnie told this story of his experience.

The chess game had got to this position:

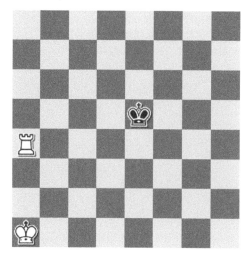

The white rook did not know how to do a checkmate so he just kept checking the black King. The game continued as follows.

1.	Ra5+	Kd6
2.	Ra6+	Kc5
3.	Ra5+	Kb4 (Help said Ronnie. He is attacking me and I cannot check him anymore. You need my help to make a checkmate said the white King. Move away on the fifth rank and I will come and help.)
4.	Rh5	Kc4
5.	Kb2	Kd4 (Black tries to stay near the central squares of the board)
6.	Kb3	Ke4
7.	Kc3	Kf4
8.	Kd3	Kg4 (attacks the rook)
9.	Ra5	Kf4
10.	Rb5	Kf3 (The black King tries to stay away from the side of board for as long as possible)
11.	Rf5+	Kg4 (attacks the rook and the white King protects the rook)
12.	Ke4	Kg3 (stays away from board side)
13.	Rg5+	Kf2
14.	Rg4	Ke2
15.	Rg2+	Kf1 (attacks the rook)
16.	Kf3	Ke1
17.	Rh2	Kd1
18.	Ke3	Kc1
19.	Kd3	Kb1 (once the black King is on the side of the board the white King moves along the third rank until the black King reaches the corner and has to move back to the b1 square)
20.	Kc3	Ka1
21.	Kb3	Kb1
22.	Rh1++	

Chapter 16

What is the Good of Gaining Material if you are then Checkmated?

One early evening there was an interesting, light hearted debate between the knights and bishops arguing which pieces were better for attacks on the f2 and f7 squares.

In this game the bishops were there at the mate.

J Reinisch   Karel Traxler (Houston, 1890)

1. e4   e5

2. Nf3   Nc6

3. Bc4   Nf6

4. Ng5   Bc5 (develops a piece rather than moving a piece twice)

5.	NXf7	BXf2+
6.	Ke2	Nd4+
7.	Kd3	b5
8.	Bb3	Nxe4
9.	NXd8	Nc5+ (Black has lost his Queen but a mating net is closing in)
10.	Kc3	Ne2+
11.	Qxe2	Bd4+
12.	Kb4	a5+
13.	KXb5	Ba6+
14.	Kxa5	Bd3+
15.	Kb4	Na6+
16.	Ka4	Nb4+
17.	KXb4	c5++ (Black is 16 points down but checkmated white)

Chapter 17

Exercises

<u>Checkmates</u>

Chess players need to know the common mating patterns.

The diagrams show the initial position and have a label saying what side is to move. In deciding which of your pieces to move see which one can move and give a check. Also see what reply your opponent has. Can they move their King out check? Can they block your check? Can they capture the piece that is checking of their King?

A <u>One move checkmates</u>

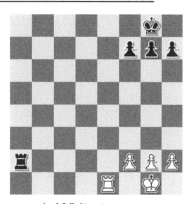

1. White to move

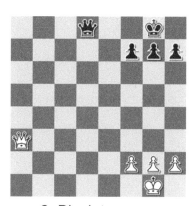

2. Black to move

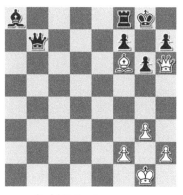

3. White to move

4. Black to move

5. White to move

6. Black to move

7. White to move

8. Black to move

9. White to move

10. Black to move

11. White to move

12. Black to move

13. White to move

14. Black to move

15. White to move

16. Black to move

B Two move checkmates

1. White to move

2. Black to move

3. White to move

4. Black to move

5. White to move

6. Black to move

7. White to move

8. Black to move

9. White to move

10. Black to move

11. White to move

12. Black to move

C Positions with mating patterns

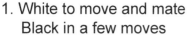

1. White to move and mate Black in a few moves

2. Black to move and win

3. Black to move and win

D End Game Positions

1. Black to move and draw

2. White to move and win

3. White to move and draw

4. Black to move and win

5. White to play and win

6. Black to play and win

7. White to move and draw

8. Black to move and win

9. White to move and win

10. Black to move and win

11. Black to move and win

Chapter 18

Answers

<u>A Note on Notation</u>

A White Move is indicated for example as 1. Qg7 and a Black Move is indicated as 1. --- Rh8

A One Move Checkmates

1.   White plays Re8 mate

2.   Black plays Qd1 mate

3.   White plays Qg7 mate

4.   Black plays Qg2 mate

5.   White plays Rh8 mate

6.   Black plays QXg2 mate

7.   White plays Qd8 mate

8.   Black plays QXg2 mate

9.   White plays Rf8 mate

10.   Black plays Rf1 mate

11.   White plays Qc7 mate

12.   Black plays Qg2 mate

13.   White plays Qg7 mate

14.   Black plays Qg2 mate

15.   White plays Nf7 mate

16.   Black plays Nf3 mate

B Two Move Checkmates

1. White plays 1. RXh7+ Kg8 2. Rag7 mate

2. Black plays 1. --- Qf2+ 2. Kh1 QXe1 mate

3. White plays 1. Qg8+ RXg8 2. Nf7 mate

4. Black plays 1. --- Qe2+ 2. Kc1 Qc2 mate

5. White plays 1. Qe8+ RXe8 2. RXe8 mate

6. Black plays 1. --- Bd4+ 2. Kh1 Bg2 mate

7. White plays 1. Rb7+ Ke8 2. Ra8 mate

8. Black plays 1. --- QXh2+ 2. KXh2 Rh8 mate

9. White plays 1. Nf6+ Kh8 2. QXh7 mate

10. Black plays 1. --- Qf3+ 2. Rg2 QXg2 mate

11. White plays 1. Nf8+ Kh8 2. Bf6 mate

12. Black plays 1. --- Bd4+ 2. Nf2 Nh3 mate

C Positions with mating patterns

You may find other variations to those given.

First position

White plays Ne7+. There are three possible replies by black.

a). 1. Ne7+ Kh7   2. RXg7+ KXg7   3. BXf6+ KXf6   4. QXh6+ Bg6   5. QXg6 mate.

b). 1. Ne7+ Kh8   2. QXh6+ gXh6   3. BXf6+ Kh7   4. Rg7+ Kh8   5. RXf7 discovered checkmate.

c). 1. Ne7+ QXe7   2. RXe7 Bf4   3. BXf6 Bg5   4. RXg5 hXg5   5. QXg5 Bg6
6. RXg7+ Kh8   7. Qh6+ Bh7   8. QXh7 mate.

If 2. ---BXh5   3. RgXg7+ Kh8 Rh7+   4. Kg8   5. Reg7 mate.

Second position

Black plays Bf5+. There are two replies by white one leads to a smothered mate and in the other white loses a lot of pieces and would eventually lose.

a). 1. --- Bf5+   2. NXf5 Qe4+   3. Ka1 Nc2+   4. Kb1 Na3+   5. Ka1 Qb1+
      6. RXb1 Nc2 mate.

b). 1.--- Bf5+   2. QXf5 RXf5   3. RXg7+ QXg7   4. NXf5 Qg6   5. a3 QXf5+
      6. Ka1 Qd3   7. Rg1+ Kf7   8. Rg7+ Kf8   9. Rg1 QXc4 10. Kb1 Qa2+
      11. Kc1 Qa1+   12. Kd2 QXg1   White is lost.

Third position

Black plays 1. --- c1=Q 2. RXQ RXh2 mate.

If 2. Rc7+ BXc7 3. NXc7 Qh6 + 4. Kg3 QXh2 mate.

If 1. --- c1=Q 2. Rc7+ Bxc7 3. f4 Qf1+ 4. Kh4 RXh2+ 5. Kg5 h6 mate or

5. Kg3 Qf2 mate. If 4. Kg3 Qf2+ 5. Kh3 QXh2 mate.

D **End Game Positions**

1. 1. --- Kb7

2. 1. Kb6

3. 1. Rb8 Kf3 2. Rf8+and draws by perpetual check or capture of the black pawn.

4. 1. --- Rg4

5. 1. Kh8 RXg7 2. Rf1+ Kg6 3. Rg1+ wins the black rook.

6. 1. --- Ra1 2. RXh2 Ra2+ wins the white rook.

7. 1. Kg7 h5 2. Kf6 Kb6 3. c7 KXc7 4. Kg5 h4 5. KXh4 drawn.

8. 1. --- Kd6 should eventually win by getting the opposition with the King and promoting a pawn from the pawn majority. Practice against a strong player or a computer.

9. 1. Qc3+ Kb1 2. Kg7 every time the black King is forced to move to b1 the white King can move nearer to help capture the pawn. Try to avoid stalemate.

10. 1. --- b4 2. aXb4 c4 3. bXc4 a3 Black will promote the pawn on file a to a Queen first and with the help of the black King will capture all the white pawns.

11. 1. --- Rg1+ 2. Kf2 a1=Q 3. RXa1 RXa1 wins.

Chapter 19

A Selection of Master Games

I give below a selection of famous games, some of which are from world championship matches that you may like to search for on the internet to see how the moves were made. This is a good way of learning from the Masters and deciding how you would have moved in the Games. You can see how the Masters applied the three basic concepts described in chapter seven in their matches. I advise that it is much better to learn from Master Games than amateur games where more mistakes are usually made by both players. Good luck with your own Games.

Gioachino Greco   **Unknown player**

French Defence

This game played by an Italian Master, Greco, in the early 1600s, a very long time ago, illustrates the Greek gift sacrifice of a Bishop.

1.	e4	e6
2.	d4	Nf6
3.	Bd3	Nc6
4.	Nf3	Be7
5.	h4	0-0
6.	e5	Nd5
7.	BXh7+	KXh7
8.	Ng5+	BXg5
9.	hXg5+	Kg8
10.	Qh5	f5
11.	g6	Re8
12.	Qh8++	

Note that white's sixth move e5 forces the knight on f6 away and it is no longer defending the pawn on h7.

★★★★★

Andrew Smith	Francois Philidor (London, 1790)
Bishop's Opening	
1. e4	e5
2. Bc4	Nf6
3. d3	c6
4. Bg5	h6
5. BXf6	QXf6
6. Nc3	b5
7. Bb3	a5
8. a3	Bc5
9. Nf3	d6
10. Qd2	Be6
11. Bxe6	fXe
12. 0-0	g5
13. h3	Nd7
14. Nh2	h5
15. g3	Ke7
16. Kg2	d5
17. f3	Nf8
18. Ne2	Ng6
19. c3	Rag8
20. d4	Bb6
21. dXe5	Qxe5
22. Nd4	Kd7

23.	Rae1	h4
24.	Qf2	Bc7
25.	Ne2	hXg
26.	QXg3	QXg3+
27.	NXg3	Nf4+
28.	Kh1	RXh3
29.	Rg1	RXh2+
30.	KXh2	Rh8+
31.	Nh5	RXh5+
32.	Kg3	Nh3+
33.	Kg4	Rh4++

Philidor creates a pawn mass in the centre so his King can stay in the middle defending pawns and he concentrates his forces against the castled white King. Smith makes too many weakening moves in front of his King. If on move 33 he had retreated the king to g2 then NXg1 leads to a won ending of rook and bishop against rook and after the rooks are exchanged the black bishop and King could combine to pick off the white pawns and promote a black pawn to a Queen.

★★★★★

Howard Staunton   **John Cochrane (London, 1842)**

Evans Gambit

1.	e4	e5
2.	Nf3	Nc6
3.	Bc4	Bc5
4.	b4	BXb4
5.	c3	Ba5
6.	0-0	Bb6
7.	Ba3	d6
8.	d4	eXd4

9.	cXd4	Nf6	
10.	e5	dXe5	
11.	Qb3	Qd7	
12.	dXe5	Na5	
13.	eXf6	NXb3	
14.	Re1+	Kd8	
15.	Be7+	Ke8	
16.	fXg7	Rg8	
17.	Bf6+	Qe6	
18.	Bxe6	Bxe6	
19.	aXb	resigns	

White's gambits a pawn to gain a tempo and is able to castle rapidly. Ba3 on move 7 prevents black castling and with white's strong centre an attack on black's King begins. White sacrifices his Queen on move 13 but obtains a key pawn on f6 supported by his bishop. The discovered check on move 17 means black loses his Queen. In King pawn open games gaining tempo and getting rapid development means pieces can be sacrificed for an attack on the King.

★★★★★

Adolf Anderssen   Jean Dufresne (Berlin 1852)

This famous game is called **The Evergreen Game**

Evans Gambit

1.	e4	e5	
2.	Nf3	Nc6	
3.	Bc4	Bc5	
4.	b4	BXb4	
5.	c3	Ba5	
6.	d4	eXd	
7.	0-0	d3	

8.	Qb3	Qf6
9.	e5	Qg6
10.	Re1	Nge7
11.	Ba3	b5
12.	QXb5	Rb8
13.	Qa4	Bb6
14.	Nbd2	Bb7
15.	Ne4	Qf5
16.	BXd3	Qh5
17.	Nf6+	gXf
18.	eXf	Rg8
19.	Rad1	QXf3
20.	Rxe7+	Nxe7
21.	QXd7+	KXd7
22.	Bf5+	Ke8
23.	Bd7+	Kf8
24.	Bxe7++	

There was a lot of manoeuvring in this game but white was able to castle to safety and black's King got stuck in the middle.

★★★★★

Paul Morphy   **Adolf Anderssen (Paris, 1858)**

Sicilian Defence

1.	e4	c5
2.	d4	cXd
3.	Nf3	Nc6
4.	NXd4	e6
5.	Nb5	d6
6.	Bf4	e5

7.	Be3	f5
8.	N1c3	f4
9.	Nd5	fXe3
10.	Nbc7+	Kf7
11.	Qf3+	Nf6
12.	Bc4	Nd4
13.	NXf6+	d5
14.	BXd5+	Kg6
15.	Qh5+	KXf6
16.	fXe3	NXc2+
17.	Ke2	Resigns

White's manoeuvres cause black to make too many pawn moves in front of his King.

Johannes Zukertort   Wilhelm Steinitz (New York, 1886)

A World Championship Game.

Queen's Gambit Declined

1.	d4	d5
2.	c4	e6
3.	Nc3	Nf6
4.	Bg5	Be7
5.	Nf3	0-0
6.	c5	b6
7.	b4	bXc
8.	dXc	a5
9.	a3	d4!
10.	BXf6	gXf
11.	Na4	e5

12.	b5	Be6
13.	g3	c6
14.	bXc	NXc6
15.	Bg2	Rb8
16.	Qc1	d3
17.	e3	e4
18.	Nd2	f5
19.	0-0	Re8
20.	f3	Nd4
21.	eXd4	QXd4+
22.	Kh1	e3
23.	Nc3	Bf6
24.	Ndb1	d2
25.	Qc2	Bb3
26.	QXf5	d1=Q
27.	NXd1	BXd1
28.	Nc3	e2
29.	RaXd1	QXc3
30.	Resigns	

White gives up the centre so move 9 d4 breaks the game open and white's King is stuck in the middle and one rook on h1 is out of the action. Note move ten gXf enables the formation of a long pawn chain with a protected passed pawn on d3.

Emanuel Lasker   **Wilhelm Steinitz**   **(Montreal, 1894)**

A World Championship Game

Ruy Lopez

| 1. | e4 | e5 |
| 2. | Nf3 | Nc6 |

3.	Bb5	d6
4.	d4	Bd7
5.	Nc3	Nge7
6.	Be3	Ng6
7.	Qd2	Be7
8.	0-0-0	a6
9.	Be2	eXd
10.	NXd4	NXd4
11.	QXd4	Bf6
12.	Qd2	Bc6
13.	Nd5	0-0
14.	g4	Re8
15.	g5	BXd5
16.	QXd5	Re5
17.	Qd2	BXg5
18.	f4	Rxe4
19.	fXg5	Qe7
20.	Rdf1	Rxe3
21.	Bc4	Nh8
22.	h4	c6
23.	g6	d5
24.	gXh7+	KXh7
25.	Bd3+	Kg8
26.	h5	Re8
27.	h6	g6
28.	h7+	Kg7
29.	Kb1	Qe5
30.	a3	c5

31.	Qf2	c4
32.	Qh4	f6
33.	Bf5	Kf7
34.	Rhg1	gXf5
35.	Qh5+	Ke7
36.	Rg8	Kd6
37.	RXf5	Qe6
38.	Rxe8	Qxe8
39.	RXf6+	Kc5
40.	Qh6	Re7
41.	Qh2	Qd7
42.	Qg1+	d4
43.	Qg5+	Qd5
44.	Rf5	QXf5
45.	QXf5+	Kd6
46.	Qf6+	Resigns

The opposite side castling plan works out well for White.

Jose Raul Capablanca   Emanuel Lasker (Havana, 1921)

A World Championship Game

Queen's Gambit Declined

1.	d4	d5
2.	Nf3	e6
3.	c4	Nf6
4.	Bg5	Nbd7
5.	e3	Be7
6.	Nc3	0-0

7.	Rc1	Re8
8.	Qc2	c6
9.	Bd3	dXc4
10.	BXc4	Nd5
11.	Bxe7	Rxe7 (QXe7 is better)
12.	0-0	Nf8
13.	Rfd1	Bd7
14.	e4	Nb6
15.	Bf1	Rc8
16.	b4	Be8
17.	Qb3	Rec7 (Black's position is cramped but the freeing move c5 is prepared for)
18.	a4	Ng6
19.	a5	Nd7
20.	e5	b6
21.	Ne4	Rb8
22.	Qc3	Nf4
23.	Nd6	Nd5 (The knights are now occupying good squares)
24.	Qa3	f6 (A fight back begins)
25.	Nxe8	Qxe8
26.	eXf6	gXf6
27.	b5	Rbc8
28.	bXc6	RXc6
29.	RXc6	RXc6
30.	aXb6	aXb6
31.	Re1	Qc8
32.	Nd2	Nf8
33.	Ne4	Qd8
34.	h4	Rc7

35.	Qb3	Rg7
36.	g3	Ra7
37.	Bc4	Ra5
38.	Nc3	NXc3
39.	QXc3	Kf7
40.	Qe3	Qd6
41.	Qe4	Ra4
42.	Qb7+	Kg6
43.	Qc8	Qb4
44.	Rc1	Qe7
45.	Bd3+	Kh6
46.	Rc7	Ra1+
47.	Kg2	Qd6
48.	QXf8+ 1-0	

Capablanca is more of an expert on the Queen's Gambit Declined and puts a positional squeeze on Lasker so that he has difficulty in the freeing move c5 and getting his queenside bishop into the game.

★★★★★

Mikhail Botvinnik   **Jose Raul Capablanca (The Netherlands, 1938)**

Nimzo-Indian Defence

This is a game between a former world champion and a future world champion.

1.	d4	Nf6
2.	c4	e6
3.	Nc3	Bb4
4.	e3	d5
5.	a3	BXc3+
6.	bXc3	c5

7.	cXd5	eXd5
8.	Bd3	0-0
9.	Ne2	b6
10.	0-0	Ba6
11.	BXa6	NXa6
12.	Bb2	Qd7
13.	a4	Rfe8
14.	Qd3	c4
15.	Qc2	Nb8
16.	Rae1!	Nc6 (The plans are implemented. Black aims to capture the pawn on a4 and white aims to push the e pawn.)
17.	Ng3	Na5
18.	f3	Nb3
19.	e4	QXa4 (Black looks forward to and ending with a passed rook pawn on the a file. White will expand in the centre and attack black's King.)
20.	e5	Nd7
21.	Qf2	g6
22.	f4	f5
23.	eXf6 e.p.	NXf6
24.	f5	RXe1
25.	RXe1	Re8
26.	Re6!	RXe6
27.	fXe	Kg7
28.	Qf4	Qe8
29.	Qe5	Qe7
30.	Ba3!!	QXa3 (A defender is diverted.)
31.	Nh5+!	gXh5
32.	Qg5+	Kf8

33.	QXf6+	Kg8 (If Ke8 then mate in two moves.)
34.	e7	Qc1+ (Can black get perpetual check?)
35.	Kf2	Qc2+
36.	Kg3	Qd3+
37.	Kh4	Qe4+
38.	KXh5	Qe2+ (Qg6+ does not work as after exchange of queens the e pawn promotes to a Queen with check.)
39.	Kh4	Qe4+
40.	g4	Qe1+
41.	Kh5	1- 0

★★★★★

Robert James Fischer   Boris Spassky (Reykjavik, 1972)

A World Championship Game

Queen's Gambit Declined Tartakower Defence

1.	c4	e6
2.	Nf3	d5
3.	d4	Nf6
4.	Nc3	Be7
5.	Bg5	0-0
6.	e3	h6
7.	Bh4	b6
8.	cXd5	NXd5
9.	BXe7	QXe7
10.	NXd5	eXd5
11.	Rc1	Be6
12.	Qa4	c5

13.	Qa3	Rc8 (This is the first pin. The black c pawn cannot move because it is pinned or holding its position. If it moves the black Queen on e7 would be captured by the white Queen.)
14.	Bb5	a6
15.	dXc5	bXc5
16.	0-0	Ra7 (The rook had to move because the pawn on a6 was pinned. If the pawn on a6 captured the bishop on b5 then the rook on a8 would be captured by the white Queen. That would be a loss of the exchange because the rook is more valuable than the bishop.)
17.	Be2	Nd7
18.	Nd4	Qf8 (Another pin. The black pawn on c5 could not capture the knight on d4 without the loss of the rook on c8 being captured by the rook on c1.)
19.	NXe6	fXe6
20.	e4	d4 (move dXe is not made because it would leave 3 black pawns isolated and easy to capture.)
21.	f4	Qe7
22.	e5	Rb8
23.	Bc4	Kh8
24.	Qh3	Nf8
25.	b3	a5
26.	f5	eXf5 (White has now broken the centre open and has a strong attack going.)
27.	RXf5	Nh7
28.	Rcf1	Qd8
29.	Qg3	Re7
30.	h4	Rbb7
31.	e6	Rbc7 (White now has an advanced pawn on e6.)
32.	Qe5	Qe8
33.	a4	Qd8

34.	R1f2	Qe8
35.	R2f3	Qd8
36.	Bd3	Qe8 (The Queen is restricted to moving to and fro because Spassky cannot improve his defences.)
37.	Qe4	Nf6 (The threat next move was Rf8+ If the black Knight captures the rook then the other white rook takes the Knight with check. If the black Queen captures the other rook then the white Queen goes to h7 which is mate.)
38.	RXf6	gXf6
39.	RXf6	Kg8
40.	Bc4	Kh8
41.	Qf4	1-0 (resigns)

Fischer achieves positional advantage by taking advantage of various pins to put his pieces onto good positions.

Further Reading, Chess Films and Suggested Websites

Books

I have found the following useful in my study of chess and coaching:

Chess for Beginners by Michael Basman, published by Dorling Kindersley 2001 and 2021. ISBN 9780241538432

Chess for Dummies by James Eade (paperback), 4th edition published by Consumer Dummies, 2016. ISBN 9781119280019

Chess for Tigers by Simon Webb (paperback) published by Batsford, 2005 (e book 2013). ISBN 9780713489880

How to play Chess by Claire Summerscale (hardback) published by Dorling Kindersley 2016. ISBN 9780241257265

Logical Chess: Move by Move: Every Move Explained. New Algebraic Edition

by Irving Chernev (paperback) published by Batsford, 2003.

ISBN 9780713484649

The Usborne Chess Book by Lucy Bowman (hardback) published by Usborne 2016. ISBN 9781409598442

Winning Chess: Tactics and Strategies by Ted Nottingham and others, published by Sterling Juvenile 2000. 9780806993324

Films

Pawn Sacrifice (2014), Amazon Prime, This features Bobby Fischer, an American grandmaster.

Magnus (2016), Amazon Prime. This features the Norwegian chess prodigy, Magnus Carlsen, who became a grandmaster at age 13 and world champion in 2013.

The Queen of Katwe (2016), Disney. How Phiona's life changes in Uganda when she is coached by Robert Katende to become a top player.

The Queen's Gambit (2020) is a popular Netflix film. It is the story of a young girl in an orphanage who reveals an astonishing talent for chess and the film shows how her life develops.

Websites: useful for players

www.chessgames.com

ECF (The English chess Federation) www.englishchess.org.uk

FIDE (International Chess Federation) www.fide.com

YouTube

You will find an amazing wealth of helpful videos on all aspects of chess playing

9 781915 492654